Princess Rose and Prince Rupert live in wonderful Princess Marigold Land. Also living in this land is a wicked old wizard – Wizard Weezle. He is always playing tricks on the children and their dog, Frisky.

7. Frisky danced and danced to the magic flute. "I wish Weezle would stop playing," thought Frisky. "I am getting tired of this." Weezle was getting tired too.

8. So he stopped playing the flute and then looked through his magic book to see what other naughty spells he could work. Frisky managed to take the magic flute!

9. "Now it is my turn to play a tune," thought the dog. And off he walked, playing a tune. Poor Weezle found that he had to dance after the dog. How funny the wizard looked.

10. Lots of folk came to watch, so Frisky put his hat down and soon folk were dropping coins into it. "Bravo," they called. Then up ran Rose and Rupert. How they laughed.

11. They picked up the hat full of money and ran home. "No longer do I want to toot that silly magic dancing-flute," said Weezle, and he took the magic spell off the flute.

12. The children found the flute-player and gave him back his flute, they also gave him the hatful of money. "What happened?" he said. "Some magic," laughed the children.

PINKIE

1. Pinkie Puff, the little elephant with the long trunk, was having a nice nap, when his friend Purr woke him up. "Come on, you lazy elephant," said Purr. "I have some jobs for you to do." "Oh dear," thought Pinkie, who had been dreaming about giant currant buns. But he knew that Purr wouldn't let him rest any more.

2. "The first job for you to do, is to clean the chimney of our house," said Purr. "Your trunk is just right for the job." So Pinkie puffed out his long trunk, picked up a feather duster, and started dusting the soot from the chimney. Up and down the chimney went Pinkie's trunk and clouds of black soot flew everywhere. "You were right," said Pinkie. "Our chimney certainly did need a clean. Look at all that soot!"

3. After cleaning the chimney, Pinkie thought, "Ah, now I can rest." He was wrong. "There is some of my washing to be dried yet," said Purr. "The washing line has broken, so we will use your trunk as a washing line." Once again, Pinkie had to puff out his trunk and then Purr hung his washing on it. Pinkie had to stand for ages holding the washing. While it dried, Purr sat down comfortably and read.

PUFF

4. As soon as the washing was dry, Pinkie thought he could then have a rest. He was wrong again. "The flowers could do with a drink," said Purr. You can guess who had to do the watering, can't you? Yes, Pinkie did. Purr brought him a bucket of water, and then Pinkie sucked up water into his trunk and swooshed on the flowers.

5. There were lots of flowers to be watered. When he had done that, Pinkie managed to sneak away without Purr seeing him. "Now what needs doing next," Purr was saying to himself. "I know," he said out loud. "The house needs painting. Pinkie can do that next." But Pinkie heard Purr, and thought, "Oh, no I can't." As quietly as he could he pulled a branch off a tree. While Purr went off to get the paint, Pinkie hid.

6. Now, it isn't easy for an elephant to hide. They are rather big! But using his trunk and the branch, Pinkie hid in some pink boulders and made himself look like a tree. Purr was puzzled when he came to look for his friend. He couldn't see him anywhere. "Pinkie, where are you?" he called. But Pinkie didn't answer. He was too busy having a nice peaceful nap. So in the end, Purr had to paint the house himself.

1. Rag Doll, Dancer Doll, Fairy Doll, Dolly Doll and Baby Doll live together in a dolls' house. One day, they were in the lounge when Baby held up the reminder pad. "Beefeater Doll is coming to lunch today," read Dancer. Dolly Doll looked up.

2. "We had better make sure that we have a nice lunch ready for Beefeater Doll," she said. So the girls hurried to the kitchen. They were dismayed when they looked in the refrigerator. "The only things we have are salady things," they gasped.

3. "Beefeater Doll won't like those things," sighed Dancer. But Dolly Doll smiled. "If I hurry, I can go and buy something that Beefeater Doll will like," she said. So while the others tidied the house, Dolly Doll hurried off. She was soon back.

4. "Come and see what I have bought," said Dolly Doll. In the kitchen, the girls saw that Dolly Doll had bought a lovely joint of beef. "There," said Dolly Doll popping it in the oven. "Beefeater will love that." "Yes, she will," said the others.

Dolly Girls

5. Leaving the meat to cook, Dolly Doll helped the others to clean the rest of the house. Later on the doorbell rang. Beefeater Doll had arrived. "Hallo," said Dolly Doll. "It is nearly lunch time, and we have a special surprise for you."

6. The dolls sat down to have their lunch. But when Beefeater Doll saw the joint of beef, she didn't look very happy. "Oh dear," she sighed. "What is the matter?" said Dolly Doll. Beefeater explained that everyone gave her beef to eat for lunch.

7. "It is because of my name," she sighed. "I would much rather have something else." "Well, we only have salady things," said Fairy, opening the refrigerator. "Salad, how lovely," said Beefeater. "I would love a plateful of that." Wasn't that funny!

8. So Beefeater Doll had salad while the other dolls ate roast beef. "This is lovely," said Baby. "I am sure it is, and I hope you didn't go to any trouble getting it for me," said Beefeater. But we know what really happened, don't we?

The story of

1. Once upon a time there was a beautiful Princess who lived in a magnificent castle. But she was not happy, because the palace belonged to a cruel King who would not let her leave the palace grounds.

2. One day, the cruel King sat on his throne. As usual he was wearing his cloak of donkey-skin, his proudest possession. "Fetch the Princess immediately," he ordered a servant. The servant hurried off.

3. When the Princess was brought before him, the King announced, "I have decided to marry you and make you my Queen." The Princess begged him to change his mind, but the King just laughed and sent her away.

4. "Whatever shall I do," thought the Princess. "I can never marry anyone as cruel and heartless as the King." Later that night, she put on a cloak and hurried out into the grounds of the palace.

DONKEY-SKIN

5. There, in a cave, lived the Princess's Fairy Godmother. The Princess explained what had happened. "The King is a vain man," said her Godmother. "He will give you anything, so this is what you must do . . ."

6. After listening to her Fairy Godmother's advice, the Princess hurried back to the palace. "Before I agree to marry you," she told the King, "I want a dress the colour of the sky." The King summoned his cloth-makers.

7. "My future Queen desires that she has a dress the colour of the sky," said the King. "So I expect you to carry out her wish." The cloth-makers set to work trying to mix the right colours to match the sky.

8. Sample after sample of brilliant blue cloth was brought before the King, but none would satisfy him. "The cloth must match the sky *perfectly*," he told the men. So back to work they went.

9

9. The cloth-makers worked and worked, then one day, to the Princess's dismay, they came into the King's chamber. They had managed to produce a material that matched the colour of the sky. "This is wonderful," said the King smiling.

10. Next he ordered the finest tailors in the land to start making a dress fit for a Queen. The men worked all day and all night in order to cut out the dress in time for the ball at which the Princess's engagement was to be announced.

11. A dummy was made that was exactly the same size as the Princess. And on this, the seamstresses set to work to fit the pieces of the dress together and decorate it with ribbon and lace. It was the finest dress that had ever been made.

12. At last the dress was finished and brought before the King and the Princess. The Princess would have been delighted, but she knew she would have to marry the King, now that he had got her the dress she desired. How sad the Princess was.

13. That evening, the Princess wore her new dress at the Royal Ball. All the noblemen and their wives who came to the ball thought the Princess's dress was the most wonderful dress they had ever seen. "What a lucky girl," said one of them.

14. But the Princess could not hide her sadness as she danced with the King. "You are not happy, my child," said the King. "If it is another dress you want, it shall be made, and if it does not please you, I will not make you marry me."

15. The King was so pleased with the sky-blue dress, he was ready to promise anything. When the ball was over, the Princess hurried to her Fairy Godmother and told her what the King had said. Again the Fairy Godmother told her what she must do.

16. The next morning, the Princess went to see the King. "Please, Your Majesty," she said. "I would love a dress the colour of the moon." At once the King summoned the cloth-makers. "It shall be done, Your Majesty," promised the men humbly.

Continued on the next page.

17. "To make a dress the colour of the moon, we shall need the finest silver thread," said the cloth-makers. So they went to the silver-smiths and ordered them to make fine silver thread. First the silver was melted in a huge furnace.

18. Then it was poured into a cauldron from where it flowed through a fine nozzle and hardened into thin wire. Then it was the weavers' turn to make the silver thread into cloth that shone as brightly as the moon. Soon the silver cloth was made.

19. The King's tailor took it to the King, who was so pleased that he ordered the Royal Dressmakers to start work on the dress at once. For hours and hours the dressmakers toiled over the dress doing their finest stitching!

20. When it was finished, it was fitted on the Princess. "I have never seen you looking so beautiful, my dear," smiled the King. "Surely now you will agree to marry me." The Princess frowned. She could think of no other excuse to put off the wedding.

21. But that night she went to see her Fairy Godmother once again. "I have a dress as beautiful as the sky, and one that shines like the moon," said the Princess. "How can I put off the day when I must agree to the wedding." Her Godmother smiled.

22. Once more she gave the Princess advice. The next day the Princess was standing on a balcony with the King. "I have two wonderful dresses," she said. "But the dress I most desire is one that is the colour of the sun that shines so radiantly."

23. "I can do anything," boasted the King. "Whatever you want, you shall have." So once again the King issued his orders – and this time the goldsmiths, the weavers, the tailors and the jewellers were soon busily at work, making a wondrous dress.

24. First a fine thread of pure gold was spun, then it was woven into cloth that shimmered like a ribbon of fire. To this was fastened diamonds. It was to be the most expensive dress that had ever been made in the whole world before.

13

Continued on the next page.

25. At last the dress was finished. The King was delighted when he saw it and ordered the Princess to wear it at the Royal Ball which was going to be held that night. When the Princess saw the dress she knew the King had kept his promise.

26. It was the most beautiful dress that she had ever seen. But still she did not want to marry this vain and evil man. At the ball the courtiers gasped when they saw the wonderful dress. "Now at last you must marry me," said the King.

27. The Princess did not know what to say. The King had done everything she asked, but he was the last man in the world she wanted to marry. "What shall I do?" she thought. As soon as the ball was over she ran to her room to get her cloak.

28. Then she hurried to her Fairy Godmother. "You must ask the king for the one thing he will refuse you," said her Godmother. "And that is his cloak of donkey-skin. He is too proud of it to part with it. Then, when he refuses to give it to you, you can leave him."

29. The next morning the Princess went to the King. "If you give me your donkey-skin cloak I will marry you," said the Princess. The King was horrified. "Part with my cloak!" he gasped. "Never! I cannot give you that! I will never part with it!"

30. "Then I will never marry you," said the Princess, trying to hide her pleasure. "You promised to give me anything, but now you have broken your word." But then the King got up, pulled off his cloak and put it round the Princess's shoulders.

31. "There," he smiled. "It is yours, and now you will be mine!" The Princess could not stop the tears that rolled down her cheeks. Her Fairy Godmother's plan had failed – she *had* to marry the King! He had kept his word after all!

32. At once preparations were made for a banquet to celebrate the wedding. "This will be the finest banquet that has ever been seen," boasted the King. "Everyone will come." The Princess watched sadly – was she to spend the rest of her days unhappily!

Continued on the next page.

33. The Princess could stand no more. She ran to her Fairy Godmother, and said, "The King has given me his donkey-skin cloak and now I must marry him. What shall I do?" "The only thing left to do is to run away," said her Fairy Godmother.

34. She gave the Princess a magic wand and a magic chest. Into the chest the Princess put her three dresses. "Wave the wand over the chest and it will vanish," said her Godmother, "but it will follow you wherever you go." The Princess ran back to the palace to pack.

35. As soon as she had packed, and made the chest vanish, the Princess dressed in a ragged dress. Wrapping the donkey-skin round her shoulders, she crept from the palace. How the guards laughed at the ragged girl – not knowing she was the Princess.

36. And so the Princess made her escape. She wandered through the countryside for many miles, until at last she came to a farmhouse. "Perhaps they will let me stay here and feed me if I work hard for them," thought the poor lonely Princess.

Continued on page 71.

PLAYHOUR PUZZLES

1. Can you say which child is flying which kite by tracing along the tangled kite strings? Trace carefully, won't you?

2. You need a blue and a red coloured pencil for this puzzle. Shade the parts marked with a dot blue, and the parts marked with a cross red, to see a picture.

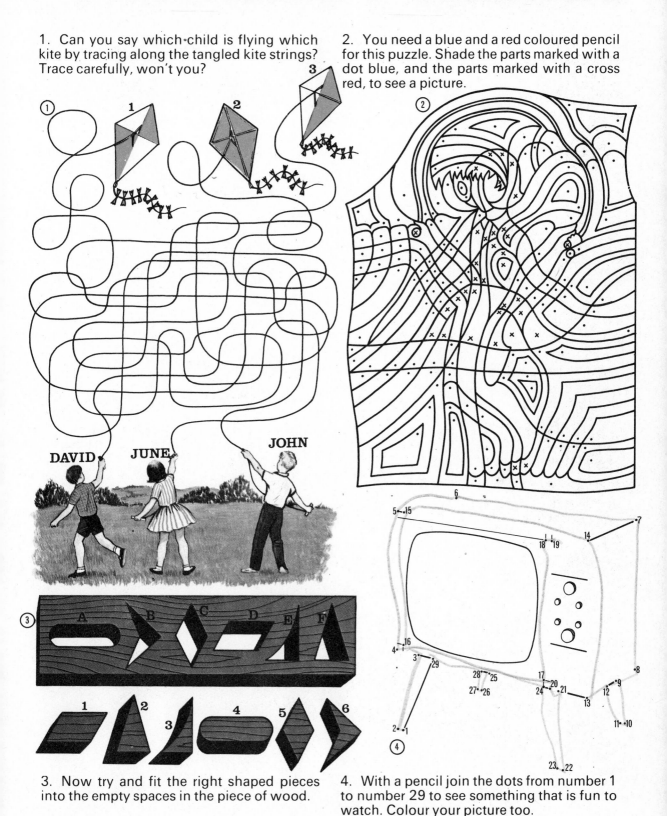

3. Now try and fit the right shaped pieces into the empty spaces in the piece of wood.

4. With a pencil join the dots from number 1 to number 29 to see something that is fun to watch. Colour your picture too.

ANSWERS:

(1) David is flying kite 3 and John is flying kite 1. June is flying kite 2, (2) Your picture showed a girl skipping. (3) Piece 1 in D, 2 in F, 3 in E, 4 in A, 5 in C and 6 in B. (4) You drew a television.

Sonny and Sally

1. Sonny and Sally live with their mummy and daddy in Happy Valley. One day, Mummy took the children to the recreation ground. Of course their pet lamb, Pet, went with them. Sonny saw the roundabout first.

2. "Let's play on that," he said. "Ooo, yes," laughed Sally. Soon they were whizzing round and round. Pet stood with a sad, what-about-me, look on his face. So Sally picked him up and let him ride too.

3. "Baaa," went Pet, wishing he wasn't on the roundabout as it spun round. "I don't think Pet really enjoyed that ride," said Mummy. Next, Sonny and Sally had a go on the swings. Pet couldn't join in!

4. Mummy saw how sad Pet was at being left out of all the fun, so she decided to look for something that Pet could play on too. Soon she saw the see-saw. "Come on," said Mummy. "Play on the see-saw."

5. "Pet can join in with this game," said Mummy with a smile. Sonny and Sally did enjoy their see-saw ride, and so did Pet. He sat with Sally quite happily. "Look at that little lamb," smiled some children.

6. Pet enjoyed himself so much, that Sonny and Sally had to give him lots of rides before he would let them get off. "There is time for just one more ride," said Mummy. "Let's go on the slide," said Sonny.

7. It was easy for Sonny and Sally to climb up the steps to the top of the slide, but when Pet tried, he found he couldn't quite make it. But as soon as he was sitting at the top, Sonny said, "give Pet to me."

8. Mummy picked Pet up and handed him to Sonny. Then, when Sally was ready, Sonny slid down the slide with Pet. "Baaa," went Pet, with a big grin. Which meant, "That was fun!" Isn't Pet a funny little lamb?

SONNY AND SALLY'S RIDDLES:

Which burns longer—a candle or a match?
Neither! They both burn shorter.

What must you do before you get out of a boat?
Get into it, of course!

Where does Thursday come before Wednesday?
In the dictionary.

19

Hans and Gretchen

1. Hans and Gretchen, the two little Dutch Dolls, were on their way to their grandma's house. They were taking a kitten to her, to keep her company. Suddenly a gust of wind blew Hans' hat from his head. "Oh, bother," said Hans. He was so busy watching his hat sail away, that he didn't spot the little white kitten jump out of the basket and scamper off down the lane.

2. Hans chased after his hat. First the wind blew it one way, then it blew it another, just as he was about to pick it up. Down the lane it sailed. Gretchen couldn't help giggling, as she saw Hans chase after his hat. "Hurry up, Hans," she called. "We shall be late for tea." At last the wind stopped blowing and Hans was able to bend down to pick up his hat before it blew away again.

3. Well, Hans was just about to pick it up, when suddenly, without any warning, the hat jumped! Hans blinked his eyes. Then he tried to pick it up again—and it jumped! Hans was completely amazed. It wasn't the wind blowing this time. No. The hat was moving all by itself. "Gretchen," called Hans. "Come here. My hat won't stop moving." Gretchen hurried up.

4. "Don't be silly, Hans," she said. "Hats don't move by themselves. Let me pick it up." But as soon as she bent down to pick up the hat, it jumped away from her. The dolls were soon chasing the jumping hat all over the lane. It was all very puzzling. "I think there is a mischievous little animal under your hat, Hans," said Gretchen. As she said that the hat jumped up into the air again and bounced off down the lane.

5. At last Hans made an extra-fast grab for his hat and caught it. "Now lift it very gently," said Gretchen. So Hans lifted the hat up and there, peeking cheekily out from under the hat was their little white kitten. The hat had landed on it! "How did you get under there," gasped Gretchen. "You are supposed to be in your basket." Soon the kitten was back there.

6. "It is just as well your hat blew away," said Gretchen. "We might have lost Grannie's kitten otherwise." Grannie was pleased when the dolls gave her the kitten. "He is a rather naughty kitten," explained Hans. And when she heard what the little kitten had done, she couldn't help smiling. "I think I, will call him Cheeky," she said. And she did.

MIMI and MARMY

1. Mimi and her brother, Marmy, were having a lovely pretend game of pirates. "Haul up the anchor," called out Marmy. So Mimi pulled in the piece of rope with a brick tied to it, and the mice set sail.

2. Then Mummy Harvest Mice called them indoors. "You have to put on your best clothes," she told them. "Uncle Mortimer is coming to visit us. He was once a captain of a ship. So you must look extra smart."

3. Mimi and Marmy got very bored sitting still in their best clothes. Then Marmy had one of his clever ideas. "Let's make our pretend ship into one that moves," he said. So the mice nailed wheels on their boat.

4. "Now we can sail to the station and meet Uncle Mortimer," said Mimi. They jumped into their little boat on wheels and were soon whizzing along. "Help," gasped Marmy. "The boat won't stop."

two merry Harvest Mice

5. Down the hill trundled the little boat. At the bottom of the hill was pond. Bump. SPLOSH—SPLOSH! The two little Harvest Mice went into the pond—right in front of Uncle Mortimer.

6. Uncle Mortimer pulled the two wet, muddy little mice out of the pond, and took them home. Mummy Harvest Mouse was surprised when she saw them. "We went to meet uncle in our boat," sighed Marmy.

7. "Oh, you like boating do you?" smiled Uncle Mortimer. Mummy forgave Mimi and Marmy for being naughty, and while they changed, Uncle changed into his captain's uniform. "Now come with me," he said.

8. Kind Uncle Mortimer took the two mice to the boating lake at the park. There he took them for a ride in a paddle boat. "This is a safer kind of boat for you two mice," smiled Uncle Mortimer.

THE MR. MEN
Mr. Small

1. This is Mr. Small. He is the smallest one of the Mr. Men, you know.

2. One day he saw there was a new playground in the park. It did look fun.

3. Mr. Sneeze had a swing and Mr. Greedy pushed him, while Mr. Small watched.

4. He thought he would try the slide that Mr. Silly and Mr. Bump were playing on.

5. But he couldn't reach the first step. Nor could he reach the swing.

6. In the end Mr. Small knew that he couldn't have any fun in the playground.

7. He went to see Mr. Robinson, who smiled and went to the dustbin.

8. "I just threw out this old budgie's cage," he said. Mr. Small was glad.

9. Mr. Robinson gave him some old budgie's toys and Mr. Small had a lovely time.

Puzzle Fun

1. Before colouring the picture of the two children and their horse see how many horseshoes you can find hidden.
2. Join the dots from 1 to 48 with a pencil to see a large ship. The kind that used to sail the seas many, many years ago.

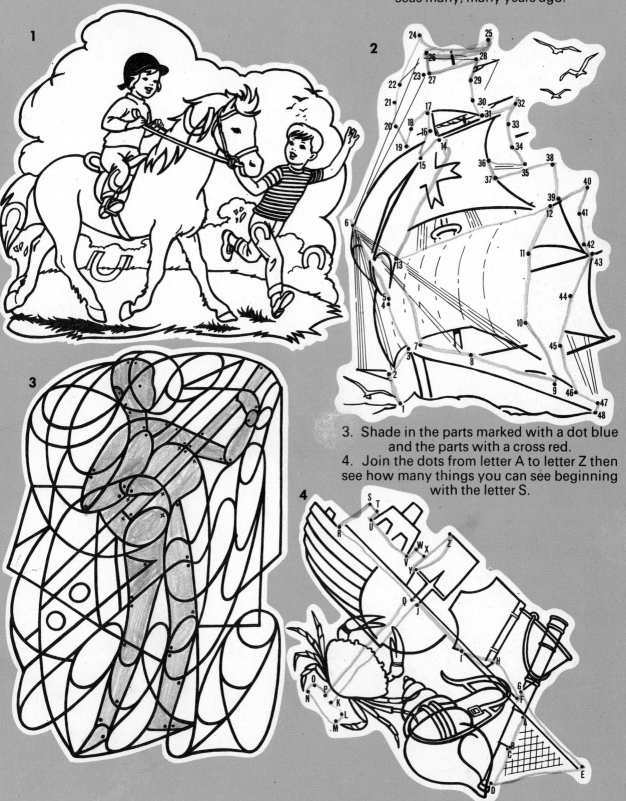

3. Shade in the parts marked with a dot blue and the parts with a cross red.
4. Join the dots from letter A to letter Z then see how many things you can see beginning with the letter S.

ANSWERS: Seashell, Sandcastle, Spade and Sandal.
(1) Seven horseshoes were hidden. (2) You drew a sailing ship. (3) You shaded in someone playing a guitar. (4) Four things started with the letter S:

1. Jenny is a little girl who has a ginger-bread boy who comes to life. But only Jenny knows this, it is her secret. One day, Jenny was busy polishing her shoes, and Ginger was helping by putting the polish on for her. After he put the polish on them, Jenny made them shine.

2. They were so busy with their work, that they did not hear some footsteps coming down the hallway towards the kitchen. Then suddenly Grandma came into the room. "Oh dear," thought little Jenny. "Grandma will see Ginger." Even Grandma doesn't know about Ginger! Ginger spotted Grandma and thought that he had better do something quickly to hide himself.

3. Then Jenny thought, "If I am quick, perhaps I could hide Ginger. But when she turned to grab him—he had gone! Jenny was most surprised. "I have just come to get my wellington boots, my dear," said Grandma. "It is raining and I want to go shopping." Jenny was still wondering where her Gingerbread Boy had gone. Can you guess?

4. Grandma found her wellington boots and then sat on a stool to put them on. She put one on quite easily, but when she came to put the other one on, she found she couldn't. "There is something in this boot," said Grandma. "I can feel it with my toes. What can it be?"

5. Grandma took the boot off again and put her hand inside it. She felt around and then she said, "Yes. There is something in here." And with a bit of a tug she pulled out—guess who! The Gingerbread Boy. "Goodness," gasped Grandma. "How did he get in there?" "I must have dropped him when I got the shoe polish out, Grandma," said Jenny. "Thank you for finding him."

6. "Well, take more care of him in future," said Grandma. Then she put her other boot on and went off shopping. Jenny gave Ginger a kiss and a hug. "What a clever place to hide," she said. "Now our secret is still safe." Ginger didn't look so pleased. "It wasn't very comfy with Grandma trying to put her foot on me," he thought. What a funny Gingerbread Boy.

Little Bo-Peep

1. One day, Little Bo-Peep was sitting in a meadow watching her father's sheep, when a little fairy flew down behind her. Bo-Peep was too busy knitting a jacket for her dolly to notice him. "I would like to try on that jacket," thought the fairy.

2. It was a hot, sunny day and knitting made Bo-Peep feel sleepy. Soon she yawned, and decided to have a nap. "Goody," thought the fairy. "Now I can try on that jacket," and he crept out from behind the tree and slipped the little jacket on himself.

3. It fitted perfectly. "I will show all my friends how smart I look," decided the fairy. So off through the wood he danced. "I won't be long," he thought. But look! The jacket caught on a blackberry bush and as the fairy ran off it came undone.

4. But someone saw the naughty fairy do that. It was Bobbie Bunny and he quickly woke Bo-Peep up. "Oh dear, where is my little jacket?" she gasped. "And where are my sheep?" Then the girl saw the wool leading into the wood and had an idea.

5. With the woodland creatures following her, Little Bo-Peep followed the trail of wool. At last she saw the little fairy sitting on the ground crying. "Oh look at the jacket," cried the fairy. "What will Bo-Peep say?" Bo-Peep couldn't help smiling.

6. "I can always make another jacket," said Bo-Peep. "But how will I find my sheep? If you find them for me, little fairy, I will knit you a jacket." The Fairy smiled and got out his flute. He played a tune and lots of fairies appeared.

7. "Don't worry, Bo-Peep, we will find your sheep," said the fairies. So while Bo-Peep sat down and started knitting a new little jacket, the fairies went off in search of her sheep. "We will soon be back," called the fairies.

8. Soon all the sheep were found, some of the fairies even rode them back to Bo-Peep. She was pleased. And as a reward she gave the little fairy a woolly jacket and promised to knit the other fairies jackets too. What a kind little girl.

Pixie Pip

1. Pixie Pip and his friends Petal and Mr. and Mrs Popple had found a house to live in. A little girl named Rosemary lived there too. One day, Mr. Popple was gazing at a bowler hat when the post arrived.

2. "Look out, Mr. Popple," called the others. But they were too late. Letters showered down on to him. Mr. Popple was surprised. Soon the other pixies were taking the letters off him. Luckily he wasn't hurt.

3. "It must be nice to get letters," said Mrs. Popple. "Let's write to each other, shall we?" said Pip. They found some doll's writing paper and envelopes and sat writing letters to each other at their home.

4. At last they had quite a heap of little letters. "Now we must post them," said Pip. Mr. Popple was worried about that. Big World pillar boxes are too big for pixies. But then they found a pixie-sized box.

5. When they had popped their letters in the pillar box, they hurried back to their home in the grandfather clock. But Pip looked round and saw Rosemary putting some money into their pillar box!

6. You see it wasn't a pillar box at all. It was her saving's box. Then Pip watched as she put it in her toy cupboard. "Oh dear," thought Pip, looking in the box. "Our letters won't arrive if it is not a real pillar box."

7. But when he saw the toy postman doll, Pip had an idea. Taking the uniform off the doll he put it on himself. Then he put the letters in the satchel and hurried to the grandfather clock and knocked on it.

8. "It is the pixie postman," said Mrs. Popple. Soon Postman Pixie Pip was handing round letters to his friends. They were excited. "What a wonderful day this has been," said Mrs. Popple. It had, hadn't it?

PIXIE PIP'S JOLLY RIDDLES

What patch does not need stitches?
A cabbage-patch.

What letter isn't in the alphabet?
The letter that is posted.

What is heavier – day or night?
Night—because day is lighter.

A WORD AND PICTURE STORY

Mrs. [hen] fluffed out her brown [feathers] and sat on four [eggs] to keep them warm. Jim's [hand] gently opened the hen-coop [door] and he peeped in. Mrs. [hen]'s bright, beady [eye] gazed at him and her [beak] pecked some corn from a [bowl] that Jim held out. The [sun] rose and set many times while the [eggs] were kept warm in the [nest]. One day, an [egg] began to crack and a little yellow came out of the . Then another chick's broke through its shell. Soon, four s nestled by Mrs. , who clucked proudly.

HERE IS THE STORY ALL IN WORDS:

Mrs. *Hen* fluffed out her brown *feathers* and sat on four *eggs* to keep them warm. Jim's *hand* gently opened the hen-coop *door* and he peeped in. Mrs. *Hen's* bright, beady *eye* gazed at him and her *beak* pecked some corn from a *bowl* that Jim held out. The *sun* rose and set many times while the *eggs* were kept warm in the *nest*. One day, an *egg* began to crack and a little yellow *chick* came out of the *broken egg*. Then another chick's *head* broke through its shell. Soon, four *chicks* nestled by Mrs. Hen who clucked proudly.

 # WILLIE WISP

Willie Wisp, the straw doll, was having a nice rest in the shade of a tree. But Billy Goat woke him up. He woke him by nibbling at a piece of straw that was poking from Willie's foot.

"Hey, stop that," said Willie crossly. But naughty Billy wouldn't. So Willie tried to run away, and Billy chased after him. While he ran, Willie joined a running race—and he won that race!

Willie was pleased when the mayor of Toy Town gave him a big basket of fruit as a prize. But he wasn't pleased about the juicy fruit, he had seen something he liked more than fruit.

The funny straw doll had seen the basket which was made of straw. Willie loves eating straw. So he gave the fruit to the runners and Billy Goat to eat, and he ate the straw basket!

1. Bunny Cuddles, the funny rabbit who loves eating jam, went to a fair with his friend, Tiny Mole. Bunny licked his lips when he saw there were jam teas at the fair.

2. But before Bunny could go and have a delicious jam tea, Tiny pulled him away and said, "Play on the hoopla stall first." "I'd rather have a jam tea," thought Bunny.

3. But he went with Tiny anyway. On the hoopla stall was a nice piggy bank that Tiny said he would love. So kind Bunny tried to win it. He had to buy lots of hoops!

4. With his last hoop, Bunny managed to win the piggy bank. Tiny *was* pleased. But Bunny wasn't! he had spent all his money winning that prize. Poor Bunny.

5. "Now I can't have a jam tea," he sighed. But Bunny had won a *special* prize. The piggy bank was full of money. "You can have the money," said Tiny.

6. So in the end Bunny had his jam tea. And he had enough money to buy an extra-big jar of jam. "Yum, yummy," laughed Bunny, as he sat eating all that jam!

the jam-loving rabbit

7. After that tea, the two friends went home. On their way home, Bunny decided that he had better buy some more jam to take home. So they went to the jam shop.

8. But before they got there, it started to pour with rain. "Oh my goodness," sighed Tiny. "We will get soaked going home in all this rain." Bunny knew what to do.

9. He took Tiny inside a shop that sold rain clothes. "I won enough money for us to have new rain clothes," said Bunny. Oh dear, the clothes were too big for Tiny.

10. "Never mind," said Bunny, paying for his clothes. "I know something that will keep you nice and dry." To Tiny's surprise, bunny hurried over to the Jam Department.

11. "I want your biggest jar of jam and a spoon, please," said Bunny. Tiny stood and watched as greedy Bunny sat and ate the whole jarful of jam. He was cross.

12. "That won't keep me dry," said Tiny. He was wrong. "The jam won't keep you dry," said Bunny. "But the jar will." He was right. Going home inside the jar Tiny kept dry.

TOAD takes to the AIR

Based on the wonderful characters in "The Wind in the Willows" by Kenneth Grahame.

Mr. Toad had bought himself a super-fast jet aeroplane.

MR. TOAD had bought himself a new toy. But it was a rather expensive toy—it was a speedy jet aeroplane! Water Rat and Mole arrived just as Mr. Toad was getting into his plane. "Watch me fly through the air," laughed Toad, climbing into the cockpit.

Off whizzed the plane into the air.

"Are you sure you know how to fly a jet aeroplane?" called Water Rat. "Of course I do," said Toad. "It is easy." Then with a tremendous roar, Mr. Toad flew off in his aeroplane. Up, up into the sky he whizzed. Now, Mr. Toad didn't really know how to fly a jet plane properly. He thought it was just like driving a car. "Just wait until they see me, the magnificent flying toad!" thought Toad. Below him, Mr. Toad saw some folk in a field. Suddenly those folk were running for their lives, as Mr. Toad swooped down from the sky, almost touching the grass. "Whee, look at me," called Mr. Toad proudly.

Toad was a proud pilot.

Some folk had to dash out of the way.

36

Down the High Street flew Toad.

Next Toad decided to fly down Riverside High Street so everyone could see his new aeroplane. As you probably know, aeroplanes are not really supposed to fly down High Streets. But did that stop Toad? It did not. Folk were quietly going along the High Street, when suddenly there was a roaring sound and a jet aeroplane came whizzing down the street.

A man in a car was so surprised he hit a lamp post, another drove through a shop window, and another went all over the road. But what was worst, Mr. Toad was flying so low, that the back wheel of his aeroplane pulled off a policeman's helmet. The policeman wasn't very pleased. "Stop, stop!" he shouted. And then he blew his whistle and chased after Toad.

"Stop, stop," called an angry policeman.

Mr. Toad heard all the shouting and yelling. and thought folk were cheering him. "I am a clever toad," he smiled to himself. But then the plane started making funny noises, and the engine suddenly stopped. Crump, bump, crash. Mr. Toad came down right beside the police station.

Toad thought folk were cheering.

Crash! Toad landed on the ground.

37

Continued on the next page.

Everyone was very cross with Toad.

Soon Mr. Toad was surrounded by some very angry folk. And the policeman had taken out his note book and was writing in it, and looking very stern indeed. "You have been a very bad toad," said the policeman. "You have frightened folk, made folk crash, taken my helmet, flown too low, crashed in my garden. Oh, my, you are in trouble!" Suddenly Mr. Toad didn't feel such a clever toad after all. Luckily Water Rat and Mole were there to take him home. "What will happen to me?" sighed Toad. A few days later, the policeman came to Toad Hall to take Mr. Toad to court. In court were a lot of important folk. "My, what a bad, bad toad you have been," said the judge. "What shall we do with you?" "I, I'm sorry," said Toad. "I promise to pay folk back for any damage I have done." "Yes, that is a good idea," said the judge. Then he added. "But you must never fly a jet aeroplane again. If you do, you will be in a lot of trouble."

"You have been a very, very bad toad," said the judge sternly.

Suddenly Toad saw a travelling fair.

"Come to Toad Hall," he said.

So Toad had to promise that he would never fly a jet aeroplane again. After paying folk for the damage he had caused, Mr. Toad was driven home. "Oh dear, oh dear," said Mr. Toad sadly. "I did enjoy flying that plane. I really did." But just as they were driving along, Toad saw some fairground folk with their travelling fair. That gave him a simply splendid idea. He jumped out of the car and ran to the leading van. "Please bring your fair to Toad Hall," he said. So the fair was put up in the grounds of Toad hall, and Mr. Toad invited all the folk from Riverside to come to the fair—free. But what Mr. Toad really enjoyed about the fair, was that it had an aeroplane ride. Mr. Toad dressed up in his pilot's clothes, and spent most of his time flying round and round. "I won't get into trouble this time," he laughed. He was right, wasn't he?

This time Mr. Toad couldn't get into trouble.

THE MAGIC ROUNDABOUT

1. Florence, Paul and Rosalie were going to play with their ball. "Come and play too, Dougal," they called. But Dougal, who can be very vain, said he was too busy admiring himself to play. Magic Mirror heard him say that.

2. "Oh, you want to admire yourself, do you?" said Magic Mirror. "Well, I can help you there. You can admire yourself in me." So Dougal went and stood in front of Magic Mirror. "Goodness," gasped Dougal, looking at himself, "my nose isn't as big as that!" So he dashed to the other side of Magic Mirror. "I am sure I don't look like that either," gasped Dougal. How strange.

3. All the time, Magic Mirror was giggling to herself. "Come and look at this side again," she giggled. Poor Dougal had another shock. "No, no," he said. "My head isn't as big as that. I am sure it isn't!" Magic Mirror was playing tricks on Dougal. So in the end the funny dog decided to go and play ball with the children. Perhaps he won't be so vain in future!

4. Later on, Dougal was walking through the Magic Garden, when he came across a strange box. He was thrilled when he saw it. "Ooo, I wonder what nice things are in this box?" he thought. "Perhaps it is full of sugar." Dougal loves sugar. What a surprise he had when he opened the box. Up popped Jack-in-the-box. "Boo," went Jack-in-the-box. Dougal nearly jumped out of his fur.

5. "Ho, ho," laughed Jack-in-the-box. "I do love to make folk jump." "Well, you won't make me jump again," thought Dougal, going off in a huff. A little later on, Dougal found another box. This time it had the word 'sugar' on it. "I am not going to open that box," decided Dougal. "It might be that naughty Jack, trying to play another trick on me."

6. Just then Paul and Florence came up. "What is the matter?" said Paul. "Don't you like sugar anymore?" "I don't like being surprised," said Dougal. But he liked this surprise—the box was full of sugar. "Oh, yummy," said the dog. Just then Brian Snail came along, and saw a box. He nearly jumped out of his shell, when up popped Jack-in-the-box.

Licensed by BBC Enterprises. THE MAGIC ROUNDABOUT © Serge Danot.

FEEDING THE BIRDS

1. What a cold winter's day it was as Peter and Joanne looked out into their garden. They saw some birds perched in a tree. They did look cold and hungry. "Can we feed the birds?" Debbie and David asked Mummy.

2. Mummy said that she had some stale bread in the larder. So putting on their warm clothes, Peter, Joanne and David went out to feed the birds. The wind blew, scattering the crumbs so the birds hardly got any.

3. Then Debbie came out. She did look pleased with herself. "I have put some food in this deep bowl," she said. "The wind won't blow it about now." "That's clever," said David, as Debbie put the bowl down.

4. Then the children went indoors to watch the birds eat the food. But no birds went near the bowl. How puzzling. When they went outside again, the bowl was *empty!* "Where has the food gone?" said Debbie.

5. "The birds cannot have eaten it so quickly," gasped Joanne. Anyway, the children went indoors, and got some more food to put out. Then watched! Along came Bruce, their dog, and ate the food.

6. "Naughty Bruce," scolded Joanne. "That food isn't for you, it is for the birds." Bruce knew he had been naughty, and crept away looking sorry for himself. "I know what we can do," said Peter.

7. He and David went to Daddy's shed, and they were soon busy putting two bits of wood together. Peter managed to bend a couple of nails, which made David giggle, but soon the job was finished.

8. Look—Peter had built a bird table. "Now the birds can eat their food easily," said Peter. "And we can see when they need more." Then they gave Bruce a bone to show that they had forgiven him.

Weren't the children kind to feed the birds? Do you feed the birds in the winter?

PIXIE PIP
and the New Tea Shop

Pixie Pip was excited when he saw there was a toadstool to let in Toadstool Town. "This is just what we need," he told the other pixies. "And you can help me make it spick and span."

Soon the pixies were busy sweeping, and dusting, and painting, and washing, and sweeping and building. And after a lot of hard work, and quite a lot of mess, the toadstool looked nice.

"Now we can open our very own tea shop," laughed Pixie Pip. Petal made the tea, and the other pixies helped to serve. Goodness what a pickle that tea shop was. Just look.

The pixies weren't very good at serving, were they? One tripped and dropped a cake, another spilt tea over a customer. But the pixies agreed—it was a very nice tea shop.

Bonnie's Wash Day

Hallo, everyone,

It was my birthday the other day, and Mummy and Daddy bought me a super present. It was a toy washing machine.

Now, I can be just like Mummy and have my own wash day.

Peep and Bo, my two cats, were very interested in my new toy, when they first saw it.

I filled it with water and was soon busy washing my dolly's clothes in it.

When Bo saw something hanging from the washing machine, he decided to play with it. So stretching out a paw, he hooked his claw and hooked the piece of washing. Then he gave it a tug. Splosh. The washing came out of the water and landed on Peep, who had been peeping round the machine.

Peep wasn't very pleased to get swooshed with wet washing, and chased Bo round the garden.

I couldn't help laughing, it was so funny. And of course Peep forgave Bo in the end. Funny cats

Lots of love, *Bonnie.*

Meet the Field Mice

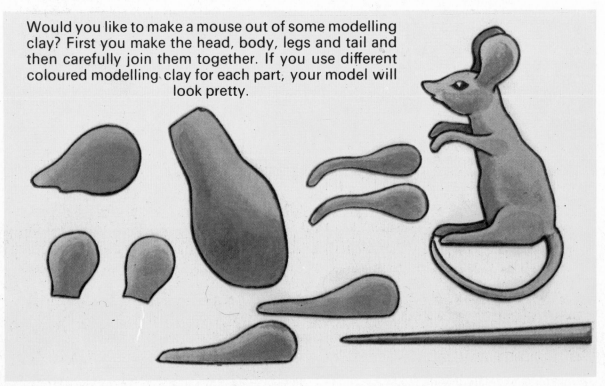

Would you like to make a mouse out of some modelling clay? First you make the head, body, legs and tail and then carefully join them together. If you use different coloured modelling clay for each part, your model will look pretty.

The long-tailed field mouse builds its nest very well. It is usually made of dry grass which is carefully woven into a ball about six inches wide. The baby mice live in this nest until they are big enough to go out. The nest is so small it is hard to spot it hidden in the undergrowth. If you see a nest, you will leave it alone, won't you?

Mummy and Daddy mouse keep the food for their young in stores under the ground, under leaves or in old bird's nests. Field mice enjoy a meal of berries, nuts, seeds and fruit. Just look at them busily eating that apple, opposite.

When you are asleep and it is starting to get dark, that is the time the little long-tailed field mouse, who is also called the wood mouse, is waking up. With his brothers and sisters, he is coming out from his home to search the woods and the fields for food. Sometimes these little mice leap along like tiny kangaroos when they are in a hurry. They will even climb trees in search of food and they use their long tails to help them keep their balance as they climb.

THE CRISP KING

THIS is a story about a King who liked potato crisps. Maybe you like them too. But you probably don't like them as much as this King did. He simply *loved* them!

The King's name was Crispin. His mother and father called him Crispin because they liked crisps too.

But they liked other things to eat as well. But King Crispin didn't. He never tried any other food. He ate potato crisps for breakfast, for dinner, and for tea every day of the week and every week of the year.

For all the people in his kingdom, this was very upsetting. Imagine what it was like to be invited to dinner by a King to find there were only crisps to eat!

The royal cook wasn't very pleased either. So, at last, he decided that he had to something about it.

As you know, most potato crisps are already salted.

The cook decided to add *lots* of salt to the King's crisps!

When the King had them for breakfast on the first morning, he thought they tasted terrible. He had to drink fourteen cups of tea to quench his thirst afterwards.

But he still ordered them for his dinner. He didn't like them then, either. He had to drink sixteen glasses of water after eating one plateful of them.

And, do you know, by the end of the day he had had enough.

Then next morning when his usual plate of crisps was put in front of him, he ordered them to be taken away.

"I want something else for breakfast," he said.

The cook sent him up some bacon and eggs, which the King found were delicious.

After that he had something different for every meal, and everyone was delighted—especially the cook.

Sometimes the King had just a few crisps after a meal, but he had learnt his lesson. Eating the same thing for every meal isn't really very good for you!

MUMMY BEAN   BOBBIE BEAN   BABY BEAN   DADDY BEAN   BUTTER BEAN   JUMPING BEAN   KO-KO BEAN

MEET THE FUNNY

1. Little Bobbie Bean lives with his mummy and daddy and baby sister in a pretty house in Beanland where the Beans live. It was Bobbie's birthday and Mummy and Daddy gave him a lovely toy scooter.

2. "Now, off you go Bobbie on your scooter to French Bean's cafe," Daddy told Bobbie. Bobbie was a bit puzzled. "Perhaps Daddy wants me to fetch something," thought Bobbie as he scooted off.

3. On his way to the cafe, Bobbie passed Runner Bean's house. Runner Bean was running round his house. "Here are some running shoes for you, Bobbie," said Runner. "Keep practising and you'll be like me."

4. Bobbie thanked Runner, tied the shoe laces of the shoes to his scooter and went on his way. He soon met Uncle Haz Bean. Funny Uncle Haz Bean had a bag of sweets hidden under his hat for Bobbie's birthday.

SOYA BEAN UNCLE HAZ BEAN AUNT HARICOT BEAN BAKED BEAN FRENCH BEAN BROAD BEAN RUNNER BEAN

BEANS OF BEANLAND

5. After thanking Uncle, Bobbie met strict Aunt Haricot Bean, who seems to frown at such a lot of things. "Uncle Haz Bean gave you sweets, did he?" she said. "I have something more useful—a soap and flannel."

6. Bobbie gave Aunt a "thank you" hug, and then carried on to French Bean's cafe. He was very surprised when he saw that Mummy, Daddy and Baby Bean were already there. "Surprise," they said.

7. French Bean had arranged a surprise birthday party for Bobbie! All the funny Beans came to that party. Can you see them? There was Soya Bean, Baked Bean, Butter Bean, who had brought butter to eat.

8. Broad Bean, Uncle Haz Bean, Aunt Haricot Bean came too. So did Runner and Jumping Bean. Ko-Ko Bean played his drums and French Bean brought out a cake shaped like the letter "B"—for Bobbie.

Lots of puzzles

1. Above is a picture for you to colour with your paints, crayons or colouring pencils. Try not to go over the lines when you are colouring, but it doesn't matter if you do.

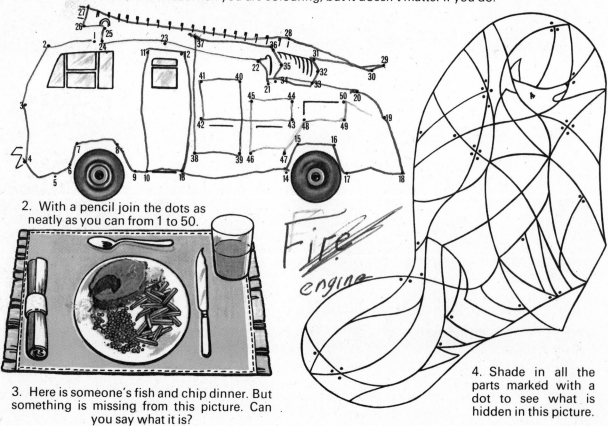

2. With a pencil join the dots as neatly as you can from 1 to 50.

3. Here is someone's fish and chip dinner. But something is missing from this picture. Can you say what it is?

4. Shade in all the parts marked with a dot to see what is hidden in this picture.

Here are the answers:

52

to puzzle you

6. What is hidden in this picture? Shade in the parts marked with a dot and something that you may have seen Daddy use will appear.

5. Here is another picture for you to draw. Join the dots from 1 to 56 to finish this picture. Colour it too if you like.

7. Which pull-along toy is each child playing with? Trace along the tangle strings from each child to see which toy he or she is playing with.

(2) You drew a fire engine. (3) The fork was missing. (4) A dog was hidden in the picture. (5) You drew a Chinese boat. (6) A spanner was hidden in the picture. (7) Girl A was playing with a train. Boy B was playing with the trolley of bricks. Boy C was playing with the duck.

53

Bobtail Bunny

1. Bobtail Bunny lives in Bunnyland. One day, he jumped out of bed, hurried downstairs, had his breakfast and then got himself ready for school. "I musn't forget my satchel today," thought the little bunny.

2. So he strapped his satchel on his back and then went and gave Mummy a goodbye kiss. "See you after school, Bobtail," waved Mummy, as the bunny set off to school. "Don't hang about. Go straight to school."

3. Bobtail was often late for school, because he was a bit of a daydreamer. As he walked along, he came to a bridge. He just had to play with a stick in the water. But then he remembered Mummy's words.

4. So he put the stick down and then hurried to school. For once he was early. "Teacher will be pleased," thought Bobtail. But then he thought, "Where is my satchel? Oh no. I have forgotten it."

goes to school

5. Then do you know what that silly rabbit did? He started to run home. He hadn't forgotten his satchel, had he? He had forgotten that he had strapped it on his back. What a funny little bunny!

6. As he ran home, he met Daddy Bunny coming along in his car. "What is the matter, Bobtail?" asked Daddy. "I have forgotten my satchel, Daddy," panted the bunny. "I must go home and get it."

7. Daddy couldn't help smiling. "Oh, Bobtail," he smiled. "You haven't forgotten your satchel. There it is on your back." Bobtail looked over his shoulder. He did feel a silly. "I forgot," he said.

8. "Now I will be late for school after all," sighed Bobtail. But he wasn't. Kind Daddy gave him a lift there in his car. "Thank you, Daddy," smiled Bobtail as he hurried into school. "Bye, bye."

TOMMY TROUBLE the

1. It had been snowing hard where Tommy Trouble lives, so Daddy said he would go shopping. "Meanwhile, Tommy," said Daddy. "You can sweep the snow off the path."

2. Tommy was pleased that he had a job to do. He likes being helpful, but sometimes when he is helpful things go wrong. Soon the little boy was sweeping the snow down the path.

3. It wasn't long before the path was nice and clear. But Tommy swept the snow into the road. A man driving his car along wasn't pleased when he saw Tommy sweeping snow into the road.

4. Nor were some other drivers who were behind him. "We can't drive through that deep snow," they told Tommy's daddy when he came along. Poor Daddy was so surprised.

5. "But Daddy told me to sweep the snow off our path," said Tommy. "I know," said Daddy, "But you should have swept it to the side of the path." That is what Daddy had to do.

6. He also had to make sure the snow on the road wasn't too deep. While he did that, Tommy gave the drivers hot drinks that kind Mummy had made. What a funny little boy.

TROUBLESOME BOY

7. Well, the next day, when Tommy came downstairs, he had a surprise. It was snowing again and there was lots of snow around. Dilly next door was waiting for him.

8. "Let's play snowballs," said Dilly. "This new snow is lovely and soft." Soon the two were having a lovely game. Then Daddy called out, "Always shut outside doors."

9. He was right. Snow had drifted into the house. So Tommy got a broom and swept the snow out again. As he was putting the broom away, he noticed that the front door was open.

10. "I had better close that," thought Tommy. But as he ran up to the door, he tripped on the mat. SLAM! The door slammed shut with a great big bang. Tommy shouldn't have done that.

11. Daddy and the postman were outside the front door. Daddy had been collecting the mail and that is why the door was open. As the door slammed, snow was shaken on to them!

12. "Hey," shouted the postman. "Ugh!" went Daddy. Tommy opened the door. "Why did you do that?" said Daddy. "You told me to shut the door," said Tommy. What could Daddy say?

1 Dagwood Duck always likes to try doing something new. One day, when his friend, Matilda Duck, was passing Dagwood's house she saw a sign outside it saying, "Dagwood Duck— Barber." When Dagwood saw her, he came out and said, "Would you like me to cut your hair?" Matilda couldn't help laughing. "Ooo, Dagwood, you are funny," she said. "Ducks don't have hair to cut—they have feathers." Dagwood hadn't thought of that.

3 First he poured some shampoo on to Uncle Cyril's head. Then he added some water, and then he started rubbing, and then he added some more shampoo, and then he added some more water. Soon lots of soapy bubbles were coming from Uncle Cyril's head. The more Dagwood rubbed, the more bubbles appeared. It wasn't very long before all you could see were bubbles and no Uncle Cyril. "Uggle, ugh," went poor Uncle Cyril. "Where am I? What has happened? All I can see are bubbles."

5 "But I wanted to be a barber and cut hair," sighed Dagwood. "But as you said, duck's don't have hair." Then Matilda had a splendid idea. "I know," she said. "You can come to my house. There is something that needs cutting there." So Dagwood went with her. She took him into her garden and showed him her hedges. They were all overgrown. "You can cut my hedges for me," said Matilda. "They could do with a trim." "I will make them the tidiest hedges you have ever seen," said Dagwood snipping away.

DAGWOOD DUCK

2 But did that bother Dagwood? It did not. A little later on, Uncle Cyril Duck came by. Dagwood saw him passing and rushed out. "Would you like a shampoo, uncle?" said Dagwood. Uncle Cyril smiled, and said, "Yes I would." So he went into Dagwood's house and sat down in his barber's chair. Uncle Cyril was rather tall, and Dagwood had to stand on a stool so he could reach his head. Then he started.

4 "I think I have used a bit too much shampoo," said Dagwood. To get rid of all those bubbles, Dagwood had to use lots and lots of towels. Normally he would have just washed them off Uncle's head. But he couldn't do that, because Uncle was *covered* in bubbles. By the time he had finished, Uncle was rather cross. "You are not a very good barber, Dagwood," he said crossly. Matilda did feel sorry for Dagwood when she saw his sad little face. "You'll think of something else to do," she said.

6 He snipped and snipped, until the hedges were nice and neat. Then he had an idea. "I know how to make Matilda's hedges look extra smart," he thought. And he started snipping away again. What a lovely surprise Matilda had when she came out. Dagwood had cut some duck shapes in the hedges. "Oh, lovely," she said. "You are a clever duck, Dagwood." Dagwood did feel proud. "I may not be a very good barber," he said. "But I am a good hedge trimmer." He was right, wasn't he?

MOONY FROM THE MOON

1. Moony is a little chap who comes from the moon. He can change into anything he wants to, just by thinking about it. He saw some party dresses on a rack in a shop.

2. "I wonder what it is like to be a party dress," he thought. So he changed into one and hung himself on a hanger. Just then along came Susan and her mummy.

3. "Oh, look at this lovely party dress, Mummy," said Susan. "It is just what I want for my party." So Mummy bought it. Back home she saw the black and white spots.

4. Everything Moony changes into has black and white spots. "I had better brush those spots off," she said. But before she could, Moony changed back into himself again.

5. Then he explained what he had done. Susan wasn't very pleased. "I haven't got a party dress now," she said so Moony changed into a box with a new dress in it.

6. It was a lovely dress, and Susan wore it for her party. Moony joined in with the games. The children played hunt-the-moony. Can you see Moony hiding?

Christmas Puzzles

1 To read this Christmas message. Hold this page up to a mirror.

ƧAMTƧIRHƆ YRRƎM

2 Shade in all the parts marked with a dot so as to see a farm-yard creature.

. UGAR   . RUIT

. UTS   . ILK   . UET

. GGS   . LOUR

3 The first letters of the things that were used to make this Christmas pudding are missing. What are they?

4 How many things can you see starting with the letter 'T' in this stocking?

DOL   HTA   RGNI   TPO   DMRU

5 Put the letters on each cracker in the right order to see what toy is in each of them.

ANSWERS:

6 Lastly you can have fun with your colouring things. Colour this picture of Father Christmas as gaily as you can. Don't forget to colour the picture's frame, then you can cut it out and hang it up in your room.

Hans and Gretchen

1. "Let's go mushrooming today," Gretchen said to her brother, Hans. "That is a good idea," said Hans. "But it looks as though it might rain, so we had better take an umbrella." Gretchen said she would take the biggest umbrella she could find. "You can carry the basket, and I will carry the umbrella," she said. So off they went to a field where they knew there were plenty of mushrooms. They were busy picking them when suddenly it started to rain.

2. "It is lucky you thought of bringing an umbrella," said Gretchen. "Well, I have filled the basket with mushrooms," said Hans. "So we can go home now." The two Dutch Dolls set off home. But oh dear, look what happened on the way. Gretchen didn't see the low-hanging branch of a tree, and before she could do anything, the sharp branches had torn lots of holes in their umbrella. Rip, rip, rip, went the branches on the umbrella.

3. "Oh dear," said Hans. "That has spoilt our umbrella." Then the two dolls noticed something else. Now there were lots of holes in the umbrella, the rain came through them. "I am getting all nasty and wet," sighed Hans. "So am I," said Gretchen. "What shall we do? We are a long way from home and I am feeling hungry." Hans looked around to see if there was anywhere to shelter. But there was only an old windmill and that was quite a long way away. It looked as though they were going to get wet!

go mushrooming

4. But then Hans had a simply splendid idea. "I know what to do," he said. "We can use these mushrooms to keep us dry." Gretchen looked very puzzled. "Mushrooms may be shaped like umbrellas," she said. "But they are certainly not big enough to shelter under." "Oh yes they are," said Hans with a big smile. He took the umbrella from Gretchen and started putting mushrooms into the torn parts. "These are just the right size to fill in the holes," he smiled.

5. Wasn't that a clever idea? The mushrooms stopped the rain coming through the holes. "Fancy me thinking you were going to shelter under the mushrooms," smiled Gretchen. "I do feel a silly." Soon all the mushrooms had been used and all the holes were filled in. "Now we can go home without getting any wetter," said Hans. He was right. The mushrooms worked very well. "You are a clever boy, Hans," said Gretchen.

6. As soon as they got home, Gretchen showed the mushrooms to her mummy to make sure that they had picked only mushrooms. Some toadstools look a bit like mushrooms, you know. So you must never pick mushrooms to eat without asking Mummy. But Hans and Gretchen knew what mushrooms looked like and they were soon having a lovely feast of mushrooms, bacon and tomato. "Mmm," said Hans. "These mushrooms are lovely." Gretchen agreed. "We must pick some more," she said.

JONATHAN BING

Poor old Jonathan Bing,
Went out in a carriage
  to visit the King,
But everyone pointed and said,
  "Look at that!
Jonathan Bing has forgotten
  his hat!"

Poor old Jonathan Bing,
Went home and put on a new hat
  to visit the King,
But by the palace a soldier
  said, "Hi!
You can't see the King. You've
  forgotten your tie!"

Poor old Jonathan Bing,
He put on a beautiful tie
  to visit the King,
But when he arrived, an Archbishop
  said, "No!
You can't come to court in
  pyjamas, you know!"

Poor old Jonathan Bing,
Went home and addressed a short
  note to the King,
"If you please, you will excuse me,
  I won't come to tea;
For home is the best place for
  all people like me."

RAG GOES TO A PARTY

ONE day, Post Doll brought a letter to the Dolly Girls' house. When they opened it they found a party invitation inside.

"Oh, hooray," laughed Fairy Doll. "I can wear my nice new dress."

The other girls were excited about the party too. They all had nice dresses to wear – except one doll.

And that was Rag Doll. Rag likes her clothes to be patched and a little bit ragged. And all her clothes are like that.

"Oh dear," she sighed. "I haven't got a nice party dress to wear."

Well, the day of the party came, and Dancer, Fairy, Dolly and Baby Doll put on their nicest dresses and were eagerly waiting to go to the party when Dolly Doll said, "Where is Rag Doll?"

She wasn't with the others.

"Come on, Rag, hurry up," Dancer called up the stairs.

"I'm not coming," replied Rag.

The dolls were amazed.

They went upstairs to see what was wrong.

Sitting on her bed, looking very sorry for herself, was Rag.

"What is the matter?" asked Dolly Doll. "Why aren't you coming to the party with us?"

"You have all got nice dresses to wear," said Rag, a tear trickling down her cheek. "But all my dresses are ragged and tatty."

The others did feel sorry for Rag.

Then Fairy smiled and said, "You remind me of Cinderella, Rag. And you know what happened to Cinderella, don't you? Her Fairy Godmother came to her rescue. So I will be your Fairy Godmother. Come outside."

Rag went with Fairy and the others.

Outside the house, Fairy waved her wand, said a few magic words, and suddenly Rag found herself in a beautiful dress sitting in a pony cart. So in the end Rag did go to the party and what a lovely time the girls had there!

NUM NUM and

1. Num Num and his brother, Drag-a-chair Puss-cat were going out with their mummy to meet Cousin Copy Cat. ''Oh dear,'' said Mummy, when she opened the door. ''It is starting to rain. We'll need an umbrella.''

2. Num Num got Mummy's umbrella and off they set. Now, not only was it raining, but it was also windy. Mummy had to hold her umbrella in front of her as they walked into the wind. ''Look out,'' said Num Num.

3. Mummy had almost gone into a lamp post! She couldn't see where she was going. Drag-a-chair, who drags his chair wherever he goes, put his chair over his head. Then Mummy's umbrella blew inside-out!

4. Luckily the cats were near an umbrella shop. ''I need a new umbrella,'' Mummy told the Umbrella Shop Cat. ''And I think I will buy Num Num and Drag-a-chair umbrellas too.'' Num Num saw a nice umbrella.

his funny family

5. "This is the umbrella I would like," said Num Num. "I can see through it when I hold it over my head." It was a see-through umbrella! "I think I would like one too," said Mummy. Drag-a-chair grinned.

6. In the end Mummy bought each of them a see-through umbrella. Then off they went to meet Copy Cat. "These umbrellas are good," smiled Mummy. "We keep nice and dry, and we can see where we are going."

7. As they were walking along, Num Num saw Copy Cat. She was in a cafe. "I can see Copy Cat sheltering in that cafe," said Num Num. "Well, let's go and join her," said Mummy with a smile.

8. So the puss-cats went into the cafe and sat down and had a drink. "Look at Copy Cat," laughed Num Num. Copy Cat was copying the waiter in the cafe. She loves to copy folk. What a funny cat.

Sally and Jake

1. Sally and Jake live with their mummy and daddy in a place called Dimbledale. Daddy owns the greengrocer's shop. "Please take these vegetables to Grannie on your trolly for me," said Daddy to Sally and Jake.

2. Sally and Jake were pleased to help Daddy. On their way to Grannie's house, they saw their friend, Harry. He was wearing roller skates. "Aren't I a good skater?" said Harry. "You just watch me."

3. Harry skated up and down and then twirled round and round. "How's that then!" he grinned. "Very good," said Sally and Jake, clapping their hands. But Jake let go of the trolly and it rolled away!

4. Harry spotted the runaway trolly. "Your trolly is going towards the duck pond," said Harry, skating after it. "Oh dear," sighed Jake. "Silly boy," said Sally. "Grannie's vegetables will get wet."

from Dimbledale

5. But she was wrong. Harry caught up with the trolly, picked it up and then jumped into the air. Whee! Right over the pond leapt Harry. "What a super jump, Harry," said Sally and Jake, looking worried.

6. Harry landed on the other side of the pond, wobbled a bit, and then sat down with a bump. "You saved the vegetables," said the children. "Aye, I did," said Harry. "Now I have something for you."

7. Harry had bought a pair of roller skates each for Sally and Jake. Jake put his on, while Harry put Sally's on for her. "Now we can roll along to Grannie's," said Harry with a grin. What fun.

8. Sally and Jake found it a bit wobbly on the skates, so Harry pulled the trolly for them. "Goodness, everything is on wheels," grinned Grannie. "I'm not," said Sly the cat. "I'm having a nice nap."

BIRDS and their EGGS

ON this page you can see some birds and their eggs. They are birds you can see almost anywhere in Britain. At the top you can see Mrs. Sparrow perched above her nest. She has laid four pale blue eggs that will be hatched into baby sparrows. If you ever find a bird's nest, leave it alone and do not disturb any bird that may be sitting on it. Below you can see other pretty birds with their eggs. First is the robin and her pink speckled egg, then below her is a blackbird and her egg. Just above the blackbird you can see a jay with her egg beside her, the bullfinch is the little bird below. Hanging upside down from that branch is the blue titmouse, she has a tiny red speckled egg, then below is a song thrush and her egg. Lastly you can see the magpie, isn't she a large bird and hasn't she got a big egg? Why don't you sit quietly in your garden one afternoon and see how many of these birds you can spot. And don't forget to feed the birds during the winter when it is hard for them to find food.

37. But as soon as the farmer saw the ragged girl, he sent her round to the back of the house. There, a fat bad-tempered cook told her she could work in the scullery washing dishes. "I want them scrubbed spotless," the old cook told her.

38. The poor Princess had never done such work in her life before. Although she had been a prisoner at the palace, she had had servants to wait on her. But now she had to work. She scrubbed and scoured the dishes until her hands were red and sore.

39. The weeks went by, working all day, with hardly a moment's rest. But in the evenings the Princess would wave her magic wand to make her chest of beautiful dresses appear. These were the only things she had to remind her of her life of luxury.

40. She took them out, one by one, and held them up against herself and gazed into a piece of mirror on the wall. Then she would remember that if she had not run away she would have been married to a wicked old King instead of a handsome Prince.

Continued on the next page.

41. So with a sigh the Princess put the three beautiful dresses, one the colour of the sky, one the colour of the moon and one the colour of the sun, back into her magic vanishing chest and carried on with her work. One day a handsome Prince visited the farm.

42. As he arrived the Princess was crossing the farmyard wearing her donkey-skin cloak. As soon as she saw him, the Princess fell in love with the handsome Prince. But the Prince was more interested in a cage full of pretty birds than a ragged servant girl.

43. The Prince lived in a palace not far from the farm. Now, one day, he was riding past when through the window of the farmhouse he got a glimpse of a lovely girl wearing a beautiful golden dress. "Who is that beautiful girl?" he thought.

44. Of course it was the Princess, wearing one of her dresses as the Prince passed. When the Prince saw her through the window he fell in love with her and wanted to make her his wife. But first he had to find out who this girl was.

45. As quickly as he could he found the farmer and asked him who lived in the room he had just passed. "That is Donkey-Skin's room," said the farmer. "There she is now." And he pointed to the ragged girl hurrying across the yard.

46. "We call her Donkey-Skin because of the cloak she wears," chuckled the farmer. "Surely this isn't the same girl I saw through the window," thought the Prince. He was so shocked that he took to his bed, sure that a magic spell had been cast on him.

47. No one could understand his illness. A few days later the cook told the Princess about the Prince's illness. "I am making a cake to cheer him up," said the cook. "He loves my cakes." Seeing the cake being made gave the Princess an idea.

48. While the cook's back was turned, she slipped her ring into the cake mix. She wanted to tell the Prince who she really was, but knew that no one would believe that she was a Princess working as a servant. But she wanted to see the Prince.

Continued on the next page.

49. Suddenly the cook turned. "Don't just stand there, girl," she said crossly. "Take the mixture to the baker to bake for me." So the Princess picked up the mixture and hurried to the bakers. Soon the cake was ready to be taken to the Prince.

50. The Princess hoped that she would be able to take the cake to the Prince. But when the palace guards saw the ragged girl, they told her to go away. The High Chamberlain took the cake to the Prince's bedroom. My, how grandly he walked along.

51. Into the Royal Bedroom marched the High Chamberlain. The doctors and courtiers gathered round the Prince's bed. "What have you got?" said the Prince. "It is one of the farm cakes that you love so much," said the High Chamberlain.

52. "Please try a piece, Your Majesty, it might make you well again," he went on. The Prince sighed and took a piece of cake. He didn't really want it but he wanted to please the others. As he bit the cake, his teeth found something hard.

53. Imagine the Prince's surprise when he found that he had bitten on an expensive gold and diamond ring. At once he guessed it was from the beautiful girl he had seen at the farm. "I want to find out the girl who owns this ring," he said.

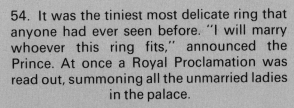

54. It was the tiniest most delicate ring that anyone had ever seen before. "I will marry whoever this ring fits," announced the Prince. At once a Royal Proclamation was read out, summoning all the unmarried ladies in the palace.

55. Now, since the Prince was not only handsome, but very rich as well, all the ladies of the Court wanted to try the ring. One by one they came forward and tried to fit the ring on their fingers. But each time the ring was too small for any of their fingers.

56. When the ring had been tried on all the ladies of the Court, the Prince ordered that the palace staff should try to fit the ring. Even the fat old cook tried the ring on, but of course it didn't fit, nor did it fit the other staff. Who could have a finger slender enough for the ring?

Continued on the next page.

57. When the Prince heard that the ring would fit no one in the palace, he ordered that everyone in his land should try the ring. So Royal Proclamations were read out in all the villages and farms. Everyone was to try on the ring the next day.

58. When all the unmarried women heard about the ring, they were very excited. Anyone who married the Prince would be rich. Some women even tried to find liquids that would make their fingers slimmer so the ring would fit them.

59. But it was all in vain. How the young women laughed, when they saw a fat woman trying to force the ring on her pudgy fingers. "You need a barrel hoop to fit that finger," laughed one of them. But the ring would fit none of the women.

60. Then at last the High Chamberlain reached the farm where the Princess was working. Each of the women on the farm tried to fit the ring. "This ring is too small for any of us women," they grumbled. "It must belong to a small child."

61. At last the Princess stepped forward. "Perhaps the ring will fit me," she said. The High Chamberlain stared at the ragged girl with the donkey-skin cloak. "Even if it did fit," he said, "the Prince could not marry a ragged urchin like you."

62. "But the Prince said that *everyone* was to try on the ring," said the Princess. So she was allowed to try the ring. Of course it fitted! How everyone gasped. "Now the Prince will have to marry this wretched girl," muttered the Chamberlain.

63. "Come to the palace," he said out loud. But the Princess said, "Wait a moment. First I must change." She went indoors. "What can that girl have to wear that will suit a Prince?" said the folk. But they were in for a surprise, weren't they?

64. The Princess put on her most beautiful dress, the dress the colour of the sun. Then out into the farmyard she walked. "Now I will meet the Prince, my future husband!" said Princess Donkey-Skin, holding her head up proudly.

Continued on the next page.

65. Everyone was quite speechless with amazement when they saw the sun-coloured dress as the sun sparkled from the jewels that decorated it. "Your coach awaits you," said the High Chamberlain, realising that this girl was not the servant she had looked.

66. The Princess was helped into the coach, and off it set through the streets of the land, to the palace where the Prince waited. "They say she is the kitchen maid who wore that awful donkey-skin cloak," folk told each other as the coach passed.

67. When the coach stopped beside the palace steps the Prince was waiting to greet the girl. "Why, you are the girl I saw for a moment through the farmhouse window," said the Prince. "But I was told you were the ragged Donkey-Skin girl."

68. "So I was," said the Princess. And she told the Prince about the wicked King and how she had run away, disguising herself as a kitchen maid, so that she wouldn't have to marry the wicked king. The Prince took her to his mother and father.